23 November 2004

Paul & Sue

Happy reading - hope you
enjoy.
Trev x

Mobil No
07966
388195

simplicity is the key

simplicity is the key

A book that you can put down

Thoughts on:

- leadership;
- change management; and
- how things get done in organisations

TREVOR GAY

Kingsham

First published in 2005
by Kingsham Press

Oldbury Complex
Marsh Lane
Easthampnett
Chichester, West Sussex
PO18 0JW
United Kingdom

Typeset in Palatino
by Marie Doherty

Printed and bound by
St. Richard's Press
Terminus Road
Chichester
UK

ISBN : 1-904235-31-X

British Library Cataloging in Publication Data
A catalogue record of this book is available from the British Library

Gay, T.

About the author

Trevor Gay is Head of Communications at Torbay Primary Care Trust, a primary healthcare organisation in the West of England and has worked for some 35 years in the National Health Service. He has an MA in Healthcare Management and is pursuing postgraduate studies as a teacher in clinical education in healthcare.

Trevor is a qualified team coach, a founding member of Rattle-the-Cage; a global virtual organisation of leaders and managers and is editor of the SIMPLICITY series of books by Kingsham Press.

Contents

Preface

This book has been in my head for 20 years.

I read "In Search of Excellence" on a train journey to a conference in 1983 and on the return journey I decided I wanted to write a book. The simplicity of Tom Peters and Robert Waterman in that classic book certainly made an impact on me. After working for 14 years in the National Health Service (NHS) I had finally discovered authors who made some sense to me. They put things over in an interesting way that was underpinned by common sense and used straightforward language rather than the language I had been learning in my 14 years at work. That language confused me, left me cold and generally made it very difficult to describe what I actually did as a manager in the NHS.

Here at last was a book that I could not put down. I continued to thumb it and I still have that book on my shelf 20 years later – even more thumbed. Peters and Waterman captured for me the essence of selling a convincing message in plain language. As I talked to colleagues about "In Search of Excellence" I was met with much cynicism. I had discussions with people who were far better read and academic than me – about the research methodology Peters and Waterman used in the book. They repeatedly argued it was not academic, full of anecdote and subjectivity. I understood the points being made by colleagues, but real life is about anecdotes and subjectivity.

Despite the lack of enthusiasm I discovered among my peers at the time, I remained sold on the style and nature of In Search of Excellence. I continued to read Tom Peters work as book after book, article after article flowed from his pen.

I was also beginning to relate common sense and simplicity to my work amid highly sceptical colleagues about the approach. I persisted and tried hard to keep things simple. I put my faith for delivery of any objective, in the people doing the work at the front line. I found myself in charge of people twice my age – they had terrific ability and experience – and I could never understand the rationale of "putting them in a box" marked "subordinate." To me, it seemed obvious that they had all the answers I was seeking as a manager, by virtue of their experience, knowledge and skills.

I also tried hard to remain grounded in healthcare by going out of my way to seek out patients and carers to spend time with them, to ask them questions about our services and then try to influence change to suit the needs of our customers. Again I was staggered by the mild (most of the time) opposition I experienced by taking the views of staff and patients or carers to important meetings.

Along the journey I was becoming more and more interested in leadership, management of change, team development and generally how things get done. I extended my reading beyond a few "like minded authors" and undertook post-graduate training in health care management.

Despite widening my knowledge and reading different perspectives from well-respected management authors, I remained more motivated by the messages of the Tom Peters thinking about simplicity. I enjoyed gathering different views through my extended reading list and realised that Peters was one of many who were advocating a new way of tackling the information revolution. However I remain convinced – 20 years later – that in many ways we are rapidly moving forward to the past where individuals are in control of their own destiny at work. Information is literally now at the fingertips of most people and the challenge for all in management settings is to justify why we are needed. What extra value do we bring that cannot be delivered by someone who costs less on the payroll? The best anecdote that struck me about the new challenge was in July 2000 when the National Plan for the NHS was published. The Secretary of State for Health delivered his speech to launch the Plan in the House of Commons and by the time he had sat down I had printed a copy of his speech and indeed the Plan itself from the Web. This was a public document and this incident made me realise that if I had the document then – in theory – so could anyone – anywhere in the world. In simple terms, the customers of the NHS and staff in the NHS were potentially as well informed as I was – now a senior manager with over 30 years experience. My mind wandered back ten years to 1990 when such a situation would not have been possible. With luck, I might have seen a hard copy of the plan within a few days or maybe weeks. The power of possessing information was illustrated to me powerfully through that one experience.

I always loved writing and took great care to keep things simple. Written words are powerful tools and the more I wrote the more responses I got, sometimes challenging my views sometimes agreeing with me. I enjoyed the banter and made a decision to try and get articles published. Needless to say to achieve publication in the "old days" – only five years ago! – the path was littered with obstacles and challenges. Comments like "lack of depth and argument" or "sounds like a management guru's pep talk" came back from editors. I tried hard to ignore those comments and searched for a market for my thoughts. Almost by accident, I approached Management Website editors asking whether they would like some articles that were not necessarily academic but reflections of my experience of operational and strategic management and policy development in health care. It was pleasing that some Web Site editors were willing to give this "school of thinking" a chance and I wrote for them. Responses to the article spurred me to write more articles and then suddenly one day it dawned on me. I simply thought, why not put these together and write the book you have promised yourself for 20 years?

So here it is. I hope you enjoy it.

What is the book about?

It is primarily about making complex things easier to understand. It is about recognising and celebrating common sense and pragmatism.

You will find the book subjective and anecdotal. It is not about absolutes or right and wrong in management. It is my view of the world of management, informed by 35 years experience of health care management in England.

It is about leadership – a subject I am fascinated by and continue to pursue my interest in. It is certainly about jargon expressions such as change management, process management and team development. Fundamentally it is about how things actually get done. It is about how from my perspective, effective outcomes are achieved. It is not intended as a one-bullet solution – I suggest life is not really like that.

It is a book that people can read in parts and put down. There will be sections that some people relate to and sections that turn people off. It will, I am sure, provoke disagreement and will be met with cynicism by some. I accept that and look forward to extending the debate on some of the things I say.

I am reminded about one of the family doctors that I interviewed during 1998 for the research that led to my dissertation **Leadership in Practice**. He felt that leadership was all about challenging the status quo, welcoming change. I agree with him. I am not a "change junkie" – I am, in fact, as conservative as the next NHS manager. I am, however, convinced that circumstances of the organisational world we now work in make it impossible to hanker for the status quo. It is just not like that any more. That thinking was fine before the information revolution – nowadays it makes no sense to me. We have two options – we either embrace the new order and make it work for us, or we resist it, and watch the world go by wondering why we have been left behind. That is not to say I believe old is bad and new is good. They are just different. It is very hard for many to embrace a totally new way of doing things and I am not advocating that change is easy to accept. It is not. Change usually presents pain at some point in the process of change for all of us. I do not suggest this massive revolution in thinking is universally popular – there are many opponents to the pace of change.

I happen to believe that pragmatists will thrive in the new environment that has developed, and indeed is still developing. My view is that the new world of organisational life presents us with a wonderful opportunity to thrive and not a threat that restricts our creativity within management. Our response to the liberating potential of the possession of information is a challenge that we will have to decide about individually. This book will hopefully add some thinking to the debates we all have to have about our response to the new organisational world.

Who is this book for?

In a nutshell, this book is for anyone and everyone. Of course the marketing Guru's will say you must know your potential audience. I agree with the sentiment but do not have the answer about which audience the book is aimed at. I believe some parts of this book that will be applicable to patients and carers. I can recognise the relevance of some parts for a cook in a hospital kitchen or a surgeon in the Operating Theatre. There are messages in the book that could be important for the chairman of an NHS organisation. Equally I can envisage a cleaner or a receptionist finding it useful to read parts of the book. Dare I suggest some of my colleague healthcare managers might even find some of it interesting? Above all though I believe that it is a book that will be of interest top-down and bottom-up.

My experience has been in healthcare but many of the messages in the book could relate to many organisational settings. The words might change for a non-health setting but the message behind the words can be applied to other organisations.

The book is unashamedly thin on research, very subjective and packed with anecdotes. That is deliberate and whilst I would greatly value feedback from academic colleagues, I do not expect much response. I do however hope that students will get an opportunity to read it and make up their minds about its authenticity and relevance, so that their learning includes a rich variety of opinions and views about the world of organisational life.

Acknowledgements

There are too many people to thank for their help in formulating my thoughts over the last 35 years working in the NHS. I risk forgetting many.

I have learned most from patients and their carers. Hundreds of them, maybe thousands, and all with a unique story. All have influenced my thinking about how things get done in the health care setting.

Colleagues I have worked with – again many hundreds – have heavily informed my development and thinking over the years.

My supervisor for the MA Management (Heath Care) was Professor George Giarchi of Plymouth University. George is now over 70 years of age – going on 18. George taught me many things – not least to remain focused. His knowledge, experience, teaching, guidance and wisdom are inspirational.

I am indebted to all the family doctors I interviewed for my research on leadership in 1997 and 1998 – particularly Phil Shute, Nick Cooper, Phil Green, Charlie Daniels, and Jill Millar.

My first boss in 1969 when I was 16 was Kenneth Spittlehouse (he was always Mr Spittlehouse) – now sadly departed. He was the Senior Administrator in a small hospital and I thought he was god. He had high standards in administration. His knowledge and eye for detail and process was incredible and I learned from him, very early in my career, the advantage of doing the basics very well. His obsession with "a tidy desk is the sign of a tidy mind" remains with me now.

Tom Peters has been a great source of inspiration and I look forward to the next Tom Peters article with the same anticipation I had when I stumbled upon In Search of Excellence in 1983.

Dr Phil Shute is my own General Practitioner, a gifted healer, a wonderful person and I am proud to say I know him – he has helped me in many ways.

Mike O'Connell is an accountant and our heated discussions are legendary – it proves to me that two people can have extremely differing views about management and remain mates. His eye for detail staggers me, and it balances nicely my occasional (of course) lack of attention to detail.

Sarah Fraser -the master of short communication – put me in touch with the publisher for this book and I will be forever grateful to her. Sarah wastes few words and thus is a brilliant communicator.

Anand the commissioning editor of Kingsham Press has been extremely supportive to me in this, my first venture into the world of writing books. His creativity and pragmatism mixed with a great sense of humour and insight make him a good friend – even though I have only known him a short time. I was very naïve going into this and I immediately felt comfortable when talking through with Anand what I needed to do. He kept me on track and guided me through what would have been extremely challenging times in getting this book on the shelves.

Other colleagues I feel the need to mention for various reasons are: Roger Anderson, Peter Colclough, Brian Ireland, Ivan Garrett, Bert Blackshaw, Ken Dainton, Brian Ward, Alan Hooper, John Mackmersh, Dr Paul Hutchinson, Dr Viv Thorn, Dr Adrian Jacobs, Dr Peter Moore, Ann Covell, Dr Liz Thomas, Dave Bateman, Dr Mike Giblin, Dr Richard Montgomery, Dr Andy Paton, Dr Giles Hammersley, Dr Simon Lansdown Dr James Bullen, Madeline Waye, Dr David Spear, Mike Wickens, Tony Boyce, Paul Courtney, Harry Gorst, Sue Newman, Helen Pynor, Ian Stuckey, Tom Williams, Dr Dev Chakraborti, Dr Rosemary Stewart, Keith Wray, Dr Antony Hignell and Dr Tony Luxton.

There are many more I should mention and my genuine thanks goes to all those I have worked with since 1969.

As this book goes to press I have to mention some very special people from all corners of the world, people with inquisitive minds and a passion and thirst for learning about leadership and management, people who quite literally stumbled across each other in a variety of chaotic ways through discussions boards on various websites.

We were motivated to exchange our views "virtually" and somehow we became a virtual team. There was no plan and no strategy. It was totally "go with the flow" … And … "this feels like a good idea."

"Rattle-The-Cage" was born. http://www.rattle-the-cage.com/index.html

We feel that "rattling cages" is really what change and leadership is all about. There are some wonderfully gifted people in leadership and management positions all over the world and many people aspiring to get there. We have to keep rattling cages to make sure voices that need to be heard are heard. Rattle-The-Cage provides that.

The rich diversity of the Rattle the Cage founders is phenomenal. The range of cultures, skills, knowledge and experience in our team is awesome. It often leaves me dumbstruck to be a part of something so special.

It is growing too. Many people are now visiting the Web Site and dialogue is buzzing – the discussion on a huge range of topics is inspiring, the learning immense.

The creation of Rattle-The-Cage is so appropriate for this book. Simplicity has underpinned our approach throughout our short existence as a team.

Rattle-The-Cage has arrived at this exciting point through the highest possible standard of professionalism, dedication, hard work and passion. But simplicity is the foundation.

It has all happened in three months
It has been achieved without a plan
It has been done through passion
It is growing
It is a modern solution in a modern world
It is inspiring
It is good fun.

I hope readers of this book will visit the Rattle-The-Cage website http://www.rattle-the-cage.com/index.html and join in.

You have loads of opportunities to comment. There are no restrictions. We welcome anyone and everyone – Rattle-The-Cage is a "community" not a "club".

My colleague founding members are:

Brian Ward in Canada
Brian Galbraith in Australia
Roger (Rocky) Noe in the United States
Adetokunbo (Toks) Obayan in Nigeria
Carlos Pereira Da Cruz in Portugal
Steve Prevette in the United States.

All of these people – and some more – have contributed greatly to get us to the point we are at now with Rattle-The-Cage. I know my colleagues will not mind if I do single out two people.

Brian Ward has done all the development work on the Web Site and is a gifted man. I am proud to "virtually" know Brian and I am looking forward to that pint with him one day. Brian runs Affinity Consulting in Edmonton, Canada. Website address: http://www.affinitymc.com and he can help you in all sorts of ways.

The other person is Brian Galbraith. Brian – like me – and indeed Brian Ward is a baby boomer (maybe that is the subject of another book) – and his energy staggers me. I believe I work quickly but Brian Galbraith makes me feel slow. He has ideas that inspire and motivate us all. He deserves great success in his major plans for his own company Optimise International. Web site address; http://www.optimise.net.au

I guess none of us know where our Cage Rattling journey will take us. That is its greatest attraction.

Foreword

For all the books on leadership and management relatively few appear to be written by people in the field, the everyday worker or manager.

With some notable exceptions (Ricardo Semmler's first hand account of the dramatic change achieved at the South American business inherited from his father, the story of remarkable growth achieved at giant multi-national General Electric as told by former CEO Jack Welch and former Mayor Rudi Guilliano's account of transformational change at the City of New York) most, it seems, are written by consultants or academics – many with useful things to say for those of us hungry for the latest management or leadership 'insight' yet almost all written from a 'third party' perspective.

This short and straightforward book is different.

Based on a first-hand experience of the UK's National Health Service (remarkably, the world's third largest employer!) and twenty years in the making, this is a book based on the day to day parry and thrust, the highs and lows, successes and failures, of life in the organisational mainstream, the day to day impacts and effects of strategies, budgets and politics, of service delivery programs, relationships and communication directly affecting the lives and well-being of sixty million 'customers' – the entire UK population.

More than anything else, this is a highly practical book.

Combining helpful information on issues of importance to leaders and managers everywhere (from the power of anecdote, analogy and story-telling in influencing people and events to the qualities and characteristics of effective leaders and managers and the way to get, *and keep,* legitimate 'power') with hard-hitting observations on the myths and limitations endemic to public health service delivery everywhere, the book should be compulsory reading for *everybody* in the NHS (all one million of them!) and indeed for all of those working in major health systems around the world.

And it should be recommended reading for anyone interested in understanding and improving their own approach to leadership, management and communication – which, as Gay points out, together with honesty, trust and transparency, underpin all meaningful change.

Parents, teachers and sports coaches will find this book as useful a tool as managers, supervisors and executives.

That Gay has managed to live up to the first part of his book's title is a remarkable achievement given the potential for complexity in such a vast subject. Simplicity is indeed the key to the success of this very welcome and timely publication.

But Gay fails in his second claim.

While he says this is a book you *can* put down, the truth is that, on a first reading, you can't.

Gay's remarkably warm; clear and conversational style coupled with his frank presentation of facts and ideas is encouraging and engaging without attempting to be simplistic or 'motivational'. While it will inspire many readers to more effective performance it will also serve as a powerful reinforcement for the millions of people in workplaces around the world who 'do the right (leadership and management) things' intuitively – as Gay himself has done over a journey of learning and discovery spanning more than thirty years, a journey he has now shared with us to very positive effect.

But Gay is right when he says this is a book you *can* go back to time and time again. Having read it through several times for this review I find myself dipping into it regularly whenever I find myself slipping into old habits (using three or more words when one will do, for example). So, in that sense, it is very much a book you *can* put down – but not for long!

Brian Galbraith

March 2004

■ *Brian Galbraith is Executive Chairman of Optimise International, a Perth, Australia and Washington DC-based international consultancy specialising in simultaneous, whole-system performance improvement for small and medium-sized enterprises.*

Trevor Gay is one of those few remarkable leaders who manage to 'get it'. The field of leadership is often regarded as complex and confusing. Trevor cuts through the clutter with his writings, which always manage to succeed at simplifying leadership.

Trevor is quick to add that while leadership is simple, it's not easy. In my discussions with him, which are always lively and to the point, he emphasises that it's people who tend to make leadership difficult. In essence, he declares that leaders often chase the latest leadership fads, which just adds to the unnecessary complexity.

He also declares, when you boil it all down, that leadership can be *made* simple, but first leaders have to 'unlearn' and divest themselves of a lot of baggage they have picked up from their past attempts at figuring out how to lead effectively. He holds that passion is more important in a leadership context than process. Too true! His passion for his subject, *simplicity,* is evident in all his writings. He walks the talk!

This, his first book, is I believe the start of something really big and exciting. His voice should, and knowing Trevor, will be heard above the all the 'white noise' that surrounds this important topic. Trevor's wit, humour and forthrightness are a fresh and lively addition to the field of leadership. Look out for more of his writings in the future.

I am proud and honoured to be able to call Trevor a friend and a colleague. I wholeheartedly endorse and recommend his writings and advice to all those beleaguered managers and others who are desperately trying to figure out their role as leaders, change agents and indeed followers.

Keep rattling the cage, Trevor!

Brian Ward
Principal, Affinity Consulting
Edmonton, Alberta
June 2004

■ *Brian Ward is author of* Lead People … Manage Things

CHAPTER ONE

The power of story telling

> Story telling – the incredible power generated by the simple act of transmitting information by word of mouth.

Sometimes I have been glued to a story told by someone – my concentration has been total. In more reflective moments I think about the process I have been through. How is it that:

- I remember the story almost word for word – without rehearsing?
- I create pictures in my head from a story?
- I can relate the story to another context and use it to transmit a message?

I am not suggesting everyone learns through stories, or that stories are the best, or only way of learning. Stories are simply one of many methods of teaching and learning – but it is interesting to muse that before the written word was invented, all information was passed on orally. Arguably, the oldest skill in the communications book of tricks is the spoken word. With the words we speak there is no electronic **spell check** or **grammar check**. When we are talking we don't think about **left or right justified** so maybe we are more 'on the spot' with our spoken word. Little wonder many like to think carefully before opening their mouth to speak – little wonder equally, that many regret speaking without thinking first. The power of the spoken word is immense.

Some have the ability to deliver the story in such a compelling way that we never forget it. I cannot recall a page of A4 text from my Physics lessons at school – but I can probably recall almost word for word, some of the stories I have been told – twenty or thirty years ago.

In the world of organisations, management and leadership I believe we are beginning to appreciate the value of story telling. Tom Peters talks about the under-estimated power of story telling in the organisational world. And for good measure there is now an impressive array of wonderful books on management and leadership that have demonstrated the power of story telling such as Blanchard and Bowles "Gung Ho", Ben Zander's "Leading as the Art of Possibility", "Fish" and "Who Moved my Cheese" amongst others.

Below are some random thoughts about story telling and its relationship to effective management and leadership and how things get done.

1. Story telling touches emotions and presses the right buttons for the listener. It is a very effective way of prompting a response and thereby creating discussion. A story can be a vehicle to transmit a potentially sensitive message.

2. Stories told well, create pictures … a picture saves a thousand words … hence, stories are an efficient, as well as effective, communication method.

3. At school some lecturers were "teachers" and some were "evangelist teachers". Though I didn't appreciate it at the time, the "teachers" were probably very competent in their subject … the "evangelists" were the ones who made learning interesting and enjoyable – part of their repertoire was usually the ability to "make it real" by telling a story.

4. Things often get done in organisations in what is called "by the way time". Those conversations in the coffee making room when the Chief Executive bumps into the Director of Finance and the conversation starts with *"By the way …"*

> " A key – perhaps the key – to leadership is the effective communication of a story. "
>
> Howard Gardner

This may not be story telling from a purist perspective but "by the way time" is ad-hoc, informal and unplanned chat … some of that will be in the nature of story telling.

5. How many times do we attend courses or conferences when what we remember of the speaker is the anecdote and the story rather than the technical information they imparted in their half-hour of glory at the podium? In my experience it is more often the story telling and the anecdote that is remembered.

6. Story telling can dissect very complex situations by providing a context that the listener can relate to. For instance when I ask a colleague in our finance team to explain some complicated financial issue to me in simple terms I usually ask for a *'Noddy' Guide.* This not only makes the subject interesting – it invariably means relaying the information in a 'story type' way.

7. In the NHS **patients and carers story telling** is one way of getting services to change. There is nothing as powerful as a patient's story and many believe it is far more effective than formal audit. Patients tend to **"say it as it really is"** and patient stories are a relatively untapped lever for change. Patients are people and we need NHS staff to deal with patients as people not as objects of clinical or diagnostic interest.

8. The "rational school" of management will argue that stories are subjective and management is about objectivity. I would say there is a place for both in many management issues in the NHS [and elsewhere] because.
   • The NHS is labour intensive with 1.3 million staff, accounting for 60% of revenue.
   • People have strengths, weaknesses and frailties.
   • People are not necessarily always predictable and rational.
   • The circumstances we operate in are dynamic.

All of these suggest a rational, logical approach will not always fit – we need some "subjective atmosphere" occasionally so that, when the need arises, we can act "on the seat of our pants" and by natural instinct, trusting only the heart. The use of story telling will be important at these times.

Many readers of this book will be aware of the legendary story of the middle manager in the multi million dollar organisation who made a mistake that cost the company 750,000 dollars. He duly arrived at the Chief Executive's office head down with his letter of resignation and meekly entered. He handed over the letter and asked that he simply be allowed to leave without the telling off he was expecting.

The Chief Executive looked at him and said

"Why would I want to sack someone I have just spent 750,000 dollars training?"

That story may have had extensions made to it over the years – is that brave and effective leadership or not?

My view is that it is superb leadership and the fact that the story is told over and over again in various settings means it is communicated to symbolically make a point about leadership. **More importantly I think it also illustrates the power of story telling.**

In summary I think we should not under-estimate the power of story telling in the world of management. It is one of the most potent weapons in the arsenal of any manager and if used sensibly, wisely and sparingly it can prove a most effective way of:

- Getting your message across
- Inspiring others
- Spreading your message
- Making work an interesting place to be.

CHAPTER TWO

Leadership and management – chalk and cheese

> There is a difference between leadership and management. Leadership is of the spirit, compounded of personality and vision; its practice is an art. Management is of the mind, a matter of accurate calculation … its practice is a science. Managers are necessary; leaders are essential.

> Field Marshall Lord Slim, when Governor-General of Australia

> Leaders say … this is where we are going … Managers say … this is how we are going to get there.

> A General Practitioner as part of interview during my research

I suggest leadership and management are as different as chalk and cheese. My views have been formed over many years as a manager in the NHS and particularly as a result of my research when studying leadership from the perspective of family doctors in 1997/8.

Good managers do not necessarily make good leaders and good leaders do not necessarily make good managers. Each has a distinct role. Leadership qualities are far less tangible and measurable whilst most management processes can be measured. Perhaps this is best summed up with Warren Bennis quote *"Managers do things right … leaders do the right things."*

There is clearly something about effective leaders that makes them stand out from the crowd. I find it impossible to identify and quantify that elusive quality. When I look back through my own career, I have had superiors who are clearly leaders and those who are clearly managers.

The **Leaders** among my past bosses:

- Have high levels of integrity
- Are focused on the bigger picture
- Are not comfortable with "intense detail"
- Make me feel part of their vision
- Do not punish mistakes – they see mistakes as a learning opportunity
- Challenge the status quo
- Are not afraid of unpopularity.

The **Managers** among my past bosses:

- Are process driven
- Are comfortable with detail
- Are more interested in the bottom line than the wider vision
- Want to measure everything
- Are not comfortable challenging the corporate view.

I think the difference is around the words hard and soft. My experience of effective managers is they tend to be very good at the "hard stuff." They are concerned with measurable outcomes – sometime obsessed with process at all costs. They appear to be driven by the need to prove their effectiveness in some tangible way. Leaders are also interested in the soft stuff – the immeasurable, the anecdote, the story.

A negative aspect of this was a story of one manager who was very stressed as he spoke to a colleague and volunteered the information that he was worried about the coming annual staff appraisals he *"had to do"* for his department. A few days later the pair met again and he was now relaxed – the stress had gone. He explained that he had now completed all appraisals – what he had actually done was take out appraisal files, ticked boxes and updated them without speaking to any member of his staff. As far as he was concerned "doing appraisals" was literally filling in forms and ticking boxes.

Effective leaders in my career are generally not so interested in the detail of process but they need to be assured there is a process. Paradoxically, the effective leader will be interested in something that may appear very trivial to "non leaders." For example, many of us have worked in organisations that proclaim:

- *"We value our staff"*
- *"We are an equal opportunities employer"*
- *"We value diversity."*

Picture now a wet, cold and dark winter morning, a 6 am early morning shift for the cleaner who parks her car in the staff car park 200 yards from the staff entrance. As she fights her way through the cold wind and rain to the entrance she notices the empty car park spaces reserved for Directors, Consultants and Chief Executive, positioned immediately outside the main entrance. She cannot help thinking the mission statement somehow just does not ring true. The effective leader will be interested in the feelings of that cleaner and even if the leader cannot solve the parking problem, the fact the he or she is interested at all, will spread around the organisation quicker than the speed of light. Quite often the leader will also solve the problem of the car parking as well. **Small things are important – leadership is not only about the big picture**.

Good leadership is usually underpinned by good management. In my experience good leaders employ effective managers and surround themselves with people who buy into the vision of the leader. The leader is always looking for improvement and though not a "change junkie" good leaders constantly question the status quo, looking for improvement. It was interesting that the first media interview with Alex Ferguson, the leader at Manchester United, after United won the Premiership Trophy for the eighth time in eleven years was full of references to *"how we need to improve this team for next season."* Ferguson is called the "Manager" of Manchester United, to me; he is the "leader." I suspect he is not interested in the intricate processes involved in running one of the biggest sporting organisations in the world. At the same time there are legendary tales of his detailed knowledge of what goes on in and around the club. It is also interesting that he has graduated to his current high standing without training in management other than in the "university of life." We can learn a lot about management and leadership by studying sport. Another famous football "manager" was Bill Shankly of Liverpool Football Club who spoke the immortal words *"Always change a winning team"* – an interesting variation of the better known saying "Never change a winning team." Again, Shankly was a leader with an impressive list of achievements and his management training was probably nil.

Both of these characters possess an ability to inspire others to sign up to their vision which, I believe, separates leaders from managers. Somehow these leaders create followers who will go the extra mile. This reminds me of the organisation where the CEO had a scheme of **GEMS** Awards for employees **G**oing that **E**xtra **M**ile **S**ervice. I guess they are all kinds of leaders and would suggest that it is not – in their case – an academic understanding of the science of management or leadership. It is probably some personal characteristic that is not tangible.

Finally I would suggest that leaders are generally born and not made. I doubt that people can learn how to be a leader from reading, studying or listening to lectures. There is something that makes leaders stand out from the rest of us. Leadership training is worthwhile. It is possible to teach leadership techniques and leadership competencies are becoming more widely used in management development. I suspect what emerges through that process will be good managers who become good leaders. The outstanding, natural leader will not need that training. Some of the greatest leaders in history never received training in the art of leadership – it came to them naturally and we should celebrate that mystical quality – even if we cannot measure it.

At the same time let us remember that leaders are in the minority and most of us mere mortals – are very effective foot soldiers – and we should also celebrate that. Many would argue wars are won by foot soldiers and not colonels. There is no question that managers and leaders are both important – both have a crucial role in organisations – but they are different.

CHAPTER THREE

Passion with a side salad of process

(Grateful thanks to John Mackmersh)

Practical ideas with built-in paradoxes

Over thirty years experience in administration (when it was an acceptable word) and management in the National Health Service, has led me to believe that the right mixture of passion and process is the way to get things done. The content of this chapter is based on personal observations and practical experience of management in the National Health Service. I believe passion, with a *"side salad"* of process, is the way – process being another word for effective action plan.

Some would argue a meal, without a side salad, is incomplete. If an outcome is a destination then three-quarters of the journey is not the final destination. A balance of passion and process can ensure we get the whole way … or, put another way … makes the meal complete.

Too much process or too much passion will often ensure non-arrival at the intended destination. But remember, individuals differ in their preferred learning styles and I do not find generalisations helpful. *"She is a process person"*… *"He is too evangelical"* … You have heard them all.

Sometimes situations call for more passion and sometimes for more process. I would say "single bullet" solutions are rarely achievable in complex organisations.

Passion can take us a long way down the road but without process, I believe we are more likely to fail. That is not to say one is more important – **simply that both are needed**.

Here are some observations about how to survive in the rapidly changing organisational environment of today. Some of the suggestions contain built-in paradoxes. I accept the difficulty that a paradox presents and I have no answers. Except that the paradoxes are there and we must learn to live with them.

The writing, publishing and marketing of this book is a great example. I was totally naïve about formal processes of writing books so I wrote this book, fired only by passion to do it. I feel that too much process would have stifled me. I would have stagnated and drowned in plans and process. The manuscript would probably have been on the shelf gathering dust for years. As it was the book was produced from nothing to retail outlets in less than six months which I was pleased with. The wonderful connections made though various accidental routes that led me to Anand the publisher definitely owed more to luck and networks than any formal plan. What a fabulous stroke of luck that turned out to be. Interestingly I did approach a publisher early on in the traditional ("correct") way – submitting a formal manuscript for consideration. I never received a reply to my letter.

The rapid production of this book was probably due, in no small measure, to my innocence of rules and regulations. I tended to simply ring people to ask simple questions and found I was pushing at open doors. People seemed to want to help me and they did. I hope I retain that simplistic and innocent approach to future writing – it seems to work.

> " All humanity is passion; without passion, religion, history, novels, art would be ineffectual. "
>
> Honore De Balzac

The secrets of success are many – this chapter highlights just a few ideas. There is no such thing as a simple checklist to ensure things get done.

My experience is that trying to keep an open mind is crucial and always being prepared to say, *"I'm still learning".* Perhaps we should consider a mission statement *"perception is everything".*

The final offering comes from someone who told me about the Managing Director who had on his desk, the traditional In-tray, Reading tray, Action tray and Pending tray. In addition he had a tray with the words *"too hard"* hand-written on the side. His theory was that if the Managing Director thinks it's *"too hard"* to understand, how could he pass the request to anyone else in the organisation? … food for thought.

Getting Things Done (in no priority order)

1.   Be determined; focussed almost to the point of being "blind" to challenge; persistent and dogged to the point of being boring … **BUT** … encourage, welcome and celebrate challenges to your thinking.

LISTEN BUT DON'T LISTEN!

2.   Ask people *and allow people* to do bits of your job … they usually do it better

WORK YOURSELF OUT OF YOUR JOB

Or, put another way …

THE BEST WAY TO GAIN POWER IS TO LET GO OF POWER

I remember when I was 23 – young and brash – even maybe dare I suggest slightly arrogant. I had got a promotion that meant I was managing people for the first time in my career as a hospital administrator.

We were pleased to get finance to employ another porter to the six-man team so that we could introduce a night shift. This was good news and I was proud that I had negotiated with my bosses to get this extra cash. Now I was spending many hours in my office with large sheets of paper writing out long hand many varieties of new shift pattern to take account of this new development. Days passed and my frustration became greater. I simply could not seem to get it to work on paper.

One of the porters – George White – who was more than twice my age and had been around a while came into my office and asked what I was doing with these large sheets of paper strewn over my desk. I explained enthusiastically that we had got this extra money for the new porter and I was designing the new shift pattern. He laughed and asked if he could have a try.

Reluctantly – realising I had to admit defeat – I agreed to let him take my feeble efforts away. Less than half a day later he came back with three or four alternative proposals and with a preferred option. He had met his colleague porters and they had done it in about an hour.

This was fabulous learning for me. The porters knew all the answers. They knew the personal circumstances of each other that made the shift planning easy.

It was another **AHA moment** for me – trust the folks at the sharp end – they always know the right answers.

3. Ask patients, carers, *users, customers and consumers* … they usually know the right answers and remember.

THE CUSTOMER IS KING OR QUEEN

4. Find older, wiser people to act as your mentor. At the same time find young, brash people to challenge your thinking.

HANG OUT WITH GEEKS AND GEEZERS

5. Try really hard to believe there is no such thing as right or wrong … there is only **difference so**.

EMBRACE DIFFERENCE

6. Write things down … they are often forgotten if not. Maybe *"basics are the new cutting edge."* (*Thanks again to John Mackmersh.*) For the Information Technology folks use "Tasks" in Microsoft Outlook – it makes it impossible to forget things!

TASK IT IN BUT THINK G-I-G-O

7. Learn to **love** modern Information Technology … **BUT** remember … one hand-written thank you note is worth fifty bland email "thank yous". (A few years ago a colleague said … *"any thank you would be gratefully received".*) In summary, only say *"thank you"* when you mean it.

KNOW WHAT TO USE WHEN AND DO IT

8.   Follow up, follow up, follow up and become obsessive about checking out things. Check the comprehension of your listener … drive your work mates mad … become a pain the neck … but make sure you do it with a smile.

ARE YOU WITH IT?

9.   Seek out cynical people and listen to them – they have a valid and important view that may differ from you … BUT … do not speak only to cynics … *the crucial thing is to be accessible and hear peoples stories*

WALK THE TALK

10.   Make sure your teams contain "exciting" people and "dull" people – celebrate their differences – they are all important people. *And remember it takes all sorts. as Meredith Belbin points out about roles in teams.*

ARE YOU A PLANT OR A SHAPER?

11.   Recruit "weirdoes" (you know what I mean) to your team. They will always challenge the status quo! *They will challenge group think. They will sometimes tell you that you are crap, but they will inject new ideas and excite new learning. And in the end you, they and the company will win.*

AVOID BAY OF PIGS THINKING

12.   Force people to change their seats. In offices, make sure people don't get too settled in one place – we can all learn from those with different backgrounds, training, skills and life experiences. *I had a meeting with a colleague recently. The location was a pleasant room with a large table and several chairs. It looked like a small*

boardroom. In one corner were a couple of easy chairs, a coffee table, a fruit bowl and some toys, squeegees and other bits that one can play with. In another corner a desk and chair, a single book-shelf and some personal mementos. It was a flexi room I thought. It is used heavily he told me and it is the office of the CEO. What happens when she is at base I asked. She hot desks like the rest of us. WOW I said, what a boss and what a role model. In this organ-isation, people don't have titles as such; they have portfolios of work that they do. I left feeling what a difference.

BE DIFFERENT: TAKE A LEAD

13. Encourage discussion, participation, corporate hugging, away days, free thinking time … BUT … sometimes, people have to be TOLD …

TELL, SELL, IM, HAVE FUN, WIN, DELIVER

14. Constantly review and adjust your own goal posts. Life is dynamic … so is work. I remember in the 1980s how I was reminded about my own resistance to change. I was a hospital administrator and the process for getting repairs and maintenance carried out in ward areas was – when I think of it now – antiquated. The ward staff filled in a hard copy form – sent that form to the admin office – who then passed it to the engineers section for action.

As administrator, this fell under my control, through a few office staff. One day I remember a good friend who was the Nurse Manager telling me he had asked the ward staff on a particular ward to send such requests in future direct to the engineers section.

I was unhappy about this – this was taking work away from admin staff who worked for me. I argued with him that this was not acceptable and the old system must remain. He repeatedly asked me why and in all honesty I couldn't find a good reason to hang on to the status quo other than "that is the system."

He was absolutely right and I was wrong. It made far more sense to "trust" the ward staff to report things rather than allow an outdated system to simply carry on unchecked.

I often wondered why I felt those internal objection that were completely without foundation. The good news was we changed the whole hospital system from the following week to bring it in line with the "rebel" ward – and efficiency and effectiveness improved – OF COURSE – **another AHA moment**.

EMBRACE CHANGE

15. Be prepared to be unpopular. If two people in a partnership always agree, one of them is not needed.

PULL SOMETIMES: PUSH SOMETIMES

16. A sense of humour is essential and a sense or proportion is required. Keep a healthy balance between work and play. Work is important; people should work hard whilst they are at work. But how many people want an epitaph that reads *"I wish I had spent more time in the office?"*

THINK AND LIVE WORK/LIFE BALANCE

17. Tom Peters once said *"Powerlessness is a state of mind – not a state of reality."* Think you are a Chief Executive … but don't be arrogant … just believe it yourself quietly. Parameters are not restrictions – they are helpful "stakes in the ground." It amazes me what power people have … if only they knew.

REMEMBER LEADING IS THE ART OF POSSIBILITY*

CHAPTER FOUR

Professional speak ... guaranteed protection

When I was younger and less confident at work in healthcare, I played the game too. I too nodded approvingly at meetings when we discussed complex issues in our own language. I probably even appeared knowledgeable.

As years have passed I have come to realise that it is in fact a game. I now try hard to keep things simple. This is not because I want to score points over colleagues or appear non conformist. It is a straightforward realisation on my part that protectionism is one of the main reasons we use such language in work settings.

I guess there is, among like-minded professionals in an organisation as complex as the health care setting, an acceptable level of "in-house" language. I happen to believe this is also an effective method of communicating among peers. Where I part company with professional speak is when the audience includes those not in the "inner circle" – in the case of health care I mean patients and carers.

Group dynamics, peer pressure and "group norming" intrigue me. One thing that has become apparent to me is that when we engage in meetings with patients and carers the language protectionism needs to be **exorcised** if we are to have real and meaningful dialogue.

I am not suggesting patients and carers are unable to comprehend complex language – that assumption would be folly and indeed insulting to the patients and carers we serve. It is simple logic to conclude that patients and carers contain, among their number, equally academic and intelligent individuals as the people serving them.

Patients and carers have enough to contend with. By virtue of entering the health care sector – the patient is in need of support, advice and guidance. There is a health problem. That is often a stress provoking position. Support and care through that stressful period of life means it will hopefully pass. I am usually very re-assured in my discussions with patients and carers that health care professionals are very good at explaining things in language that is understood by the patient or carer. There is also the opportunity for the patient or carer to check the meaning in a one to one consultation.

> So … you might say … what is the problem?
> But do also note… it is not always about problems….
> it could be about something to celebrate, share, communicate.

Something else seems to happen in meetings of managers with patients and carers.

This is a totally different setting to the one to one consultations. It can – at worst – become a stage or arena for the manager to show their prowess of mastering a language that leaves the patients and carers confused, as yet another acronym or buzz word or phrase emerges from the lips of the well meaning manager. This is not intended to be either an insult to my colleagues in management – I am proud to be one of their number – or a patronising statement about the intellectual ability of patients and carers

It is simply my contention that "in-house" language should remain in house. The moment we engage in dialogue with patients and carers outside the "warmth" of our own health care environment, the language should change to what most people would call normal.

It is, perhaps, a sweeping generalisation, and one that I am confident will provoke challenge from readers, but I suspect that most patients and carers and customers would rather hear plain language – similar to that used in everyday conversation.

"
Incomprehensible jargon is the hallmark of a professional. "

Kingman
Brewster, Jr.

This is not rocket science and I accept I am making a complex issue very simple. That is the whole point. I am simply asking for common sense and reality about the way we talk to our customers.

There are six buzzwords or phrases below that we could make a real start with. There will be numerous others that readers could easily identify. **So why don't we make a start?**

I know it takes longer to say the alternative – but maybe there is just a chance ordinary folks might understand what it is we are saying.

Professional speak	Real world language
Intermediate care	Care provided when you are too ill to be at home but not ill enough to be in a high-tech hospital. This could be, for instance, care provided in a community hospital, a nursing home, residential home or even a package of care provided in the patient's home.
Integrated care network	Hospital staff, family doctors and community health staff working more closely together to ensure patients receive their care in the most appropriate place.
Co-terminosity	Two or more organisations covering the same geographical area.
Commissioning care	Looking at the health service we buy for our population and ensuring it meets their needs and that we cannot do any better.
Governance framework	The rules and regulations by which we operate.
Annual accountability agreement	The yearly agreement between health organisations about what will be done.

CHAPTER FIVE

Ten great myths of patient and public involvement

When writing this chapter I was clearly looking at the world through my health care spectacles. I refer to the ten great myths of patient and public involvement. Clearly this is a focused chapter about the world of healthcare. **But is it? …**

Imagine this scenario …

A group of folks are chatting in a bar at the latest major international management and leadership conference. Among them are a healthcare manager; an independent management consultant; an executive from a large retail organisation; a teacher; a football coach/manager.

The healthcare manager starts talking about how some organisations in the healthcare sector seem to pay more attention to the needs of the patient and their carer than others. He passionately describes some of the myths that exist in healthcare about whether the patient or their carer should be really engaged or are they simply passive recipients of a service. He goes on to argue that there are myths in the healthcare sector about whether we should even listen to the needs of the customers – because after all "doctors always know best".

Suddenly the conversation widens and the other folks begin to contribute saying that this is true in their world. Do we really listen to what our customers want and try to deliver that or do we expect customers to fit neatly into the box that says – "this is what you need".

The scenario and context provided for the reader of this chapter are clearly focused in the world of healthcare – I contend the messages apply in almost any organisational setting.

The term patient and public involvement is confusing and difficult to grasp. The words can be somewhat unhelpful. It is difficult to measure. The one to one relationship between clinician and patient or carer is patient and public involvement. The mass town meeting of interested people, on a health service issue is patient and public involvement. Everything in between is patient and public involvement.

What it essentially is about – I contend – **is relationships**. It is the relationship in the one to one consultation and it is the relationship between an NHS organisation and patients and public in the town meeting.

William Bridges in his book "Managing Transition" describes the management of change and talks about the "neutral zone" He argues there are three distinct aspects of coping with and living through change. **Stage one** is letting go of the old – **Stage three** is accepting the challenge of the new. **Stage two** he calls the neutral zone and I suggest we in the NHS are in the neutral zone as far as patient and public involvement is concerned. Bridges neatly uses a metaphor to describe the neutral zone. He talks about being a trapeze artist and swinging through the air, in readiness to fly to the oncoming trapeze. There is a split second when we are in what he describes as the neutral zone. It is that moment when you have let go of the old – in the hope that you will meet and grab the oncoming trapeze. When you grab the new trapeze you have moved out of the neutral zone and have accepted the challenge of the new.

When in the neutral zone, as an organisation, it can of course be for many weeks, months – even years and Bridges argues this "transition" needs to be positively managed. It is in this neutral zone that people – if not shown effective leadership – will decide their own future – they will look for opportunities for their own new trapeze and you will lose good folks. Managing this transition is crucial as emotions will be running high and behaviour may not be predictable.

My experience in the NHS tells me that in this neutral zone, one of the defences created "by the nervous" is to create and develop myths. As far as patient and public involvement is concerned I am focusing this chapter on what I call *"Ten great myths of patient and public involvement"*.

It is based on personal experience, extensive reading and research but most importantly discussions over many years with patients and their carers.

This list of myths is not in order of priority.

Myth Number One: "They don't understand"

It never ceases to amaze me that this is said. There are over 60 million people living in the UK. One million of them work in the NHS. A massive workforce but almost arrogant to assume the knowledge of 1 million people exceeds the knowledge of the other 59 million. People know about their body, and therefore their health. I was impressed greatly by Alison Ryan, Chief Executive of the Princess Royal Trust for Carers. Her husband suffers from an illness that required regular injections which she performed. The Nursing profession "establishment" was up in arms about an amateur doing this. Over time she became accepted and now teaches nurses in training how to inject patients with this condition – never underestimate the value of carers.

One of my own mission statements is *"The best way to gain power is to let go of power"* – a total paradox but very real – anyone who has children will understand this phenomenon. Anyone employing staff will also understand it – get people to do your job – they usually do it better.

Myth Number Two: "Patients are not representative"

Absolutely correct and why should they be?

Patients and carers generally do not profess to be, or ask to be representative. Health is an individual matter – 'twas ever thus. We should not expect any patient to be representative. Patients and carers have enough to do without the NHS asking them to do more. It is our responsibility to find representative views – if that is possible and that – in itself – is a subject for another day. When I speak to patients and carers they do not see themselves as representing much more than their own view – which to me is all we should expect. Anything more than that is a bonus for the NHS. It is up to the NHS whether we interpret that as a representative view. Mike Farrar a well-known civil servant, in describing individuality of General Practitioners, said "There are some 35,000 GPs in this country … and if you've seen one … you've seen one" – my contention is **why should we expect patients and carers to be any different..**

Myth Number Three: "Hard to reach groups"

Some groups of the population are described as this. What do we actually mean? One such classic alleged group is young men and another alleged group is middle-aged men. In Torbay we decided to go to where those people go. In March 2003, Torquay United played Scunthorpe United in a Division Three football match. There were approaching 3000 people at the match – mainly men. Torbay Primary Care Trust decided to hold a healthy lifestyle event with the wonderful support of the Football club and take the opportunity to invite people to have a "health MOT" and engage in healthy lifestyle discussions with those motivated to want to know.

So this is not a "difficult to reach group" – they are easy to reach – the NHS seems to find it difficult to reach them – so the mission statement here is **"GO TO WHERE PEOPLE GO"**.

Myth Number Four: "Patients talk about wants: we know what they need"

My view – formed over years of listening to patients is yes, they do talk about what they want. Is it unreasonable if you are the parent of a dying child that you want to clutch at every straw – every hope – however challenging that may be to you or the service? Yes, patients talk about their wants. They do not want their child to die.

On the other hand my experience has always been that when patients are told honestly the options open to them – they accept limitations on the service – but only once they have been told the truth.

We have to think very carefully about the word "needs"– for instance – in whose interests are we really acting when we talk about needs?

Myth Number Five: "Demands will mean we can't cope"

There is a famous story about the birth of the NHS in 1948 when one health centre barricaded the doors and windows fearing they would be overrun by patients stampeding to the new "free NHS".

What happened on day one was that mums turned up in ones and twos for baby milk and the odd cold and cough nervously crossed the threshold – more out of curiosity than anything else.

I am not pretending the NHS has loads of capacity. I am just contending that patients are adult, sensible people who act rationally and reasonably most of the time.

If we can just learn to be a bit brave we may well be surprised. I well remember when a residential unit for people with a learning disability decided to allow every family to have a guaranteed minimum of three weeks respite care per year. This was more than had been offered in the past and equalised some inconsistency because some families got more than others did with no clear reasoning. What actually happened was that families did not take up their three weeks – but they knew it was there in case they needed it.

Myth Number Six: "The New Way is best"

The health service has existed since 1948. Over fifty years old and many dedicated staff delivering the service with all its warts and wrinkles. To assume that only new ways can work is naïve in the extreme.

Let me be clear though. That is not to say lets not change. I am a great believer in the new approaches to patient and public involvement and generally – I have learned to welcome change – even look for it and create it. I am nevertheless an advocate and fan of the NHS – a proud lifelong NHS worker with many friends and colleagues in whom I have great belief and faith. Some people's dedication to patients in particular, and the NHS in general, has sometimes moved me. To throw away experience as if it is irrelevant is very unwise at best and we do it at our peril. I was very attracted to a recent quote from one of my management gurus. He said he was fed up with reading annual reports that said in many different ways … "Our staff are our greatest asset… His response **"NO, NO, NO, … staff are our only asset!"**

Myth Number Seven: "It will all cost too much"

Doing things differently is one way to look at this – if we always do what we always did we will always get what we always got. I like Harry Cayton's story about dead flowers in a vase on a bedside cupboard in the hospital. It was said that we just don't have the staff to do everything. Taking out dead flowers … not a big job … lack of money and staff cannot be accepted as a reason for saying dead flowers cannot be removed.

I went to a GP and said I was very interested in this new way of getting a cholesterol test. He pricked my finger, placed the blood sample in a machine and within two minutes I had my result – happily it was ok. He explained that for patients in his neighbouring practice this would involve an appointment with the practice nurse, sending the blood to the local hospital waiting two days for the result and the patient ringing to get the result three days after having the test. I am not saying it is affordable to have this type of service in every practice. I am not suggesting this particular test is urgent enough to justify a Rolls Royce service. I am simply arguing that lack of money is always a good reason not to do things. Maybe the service needs to be braver – always remembering this is public money.

Myth Number Eight: "Staff don't have time to do all this as well"

It is my contention that staff do not need to find time to "do" patient and public involvement – they already do it all the time. All we need to do is to make sure that the NHS culture is about partnership with patients not a master servant control command relationship. Everyone has something to bring to the party – patients, staff and carers. The relationship needs to be on an equal basis. The seven-hour shift of the typical nurse is all about patient and public involvement – and if it is not – then it should be. Let patients create the rules and give managers responsibility for ensuring an easier job for staff and a better experience for the patient. IT'S not rocket science but IT IS, seemingly, not palatable to some people.

Myth Number Nine: "All this stuff cannot be measured"

Why oh why do we have to measure everything? Of course as a gnarled twisted old NHS manager, I know the answer to my rhetorical question. It is simply untrue that we cannot measure patient and public involvement. There are creative people around who can help us measure anything. Patient and Public involvement is just another challenge. If we can measure teachers and the teaching experience for children, if we can measure police productivity in crime prevention, I simply cannot accept it is not possible to measure patient and public involvement. There is work going on currently fathoming out how we can measure the most complicated processes in the world of business – we just need to be creative. This needs to be done by more skilled, experienced, creative and innovative people than managers like me … perhaps we need to ask those people … we often call them patients and carers.

Myth Number Ten: "Patients and the Public are not really interested in all this anyway"

The Audit Commission January 2003, report entitled *"Connecting with Users and Citizens"* offers an interesting insight to this.

I quote from page 4 of the report:

Ordinary folk don't want to be involved. That is a fact of life

Our own consultation with service providers highlights the difference in approach between those who feel that they are achieving a good standard of public involvement, and those who don't. For those who don't, a major stumbling block is the sense that the public are not really interested in taking part in consultation.

I rest my case – if it is good enough for the Audit Commission through valued research, it is good enough for me.

Conclusions

The NHS is changing month by month– sometimes it seems like day to day. We should celebrate this change – not create and perpetuate myths. We all have that responsibility. Your position enables you to influence your own organisation. Please take that opportunity. Why can't all Board Reports have a heading **"How have patients and carers been involved in this proposal?"**

I have always wanted to be brave enough to suggest a payment reward system for all NHS managers, based on how many patients' problems they can prove they have actually resolved in the preceding month.

Board members – particularly Non-Executive Directors – should challenge managers to justify how decisions are made without patients being involved in the decision making process.

Finally I would commend to you Harry Cayton's three messages about Patient & Public Involvement?

1. *Trust me I'm a patient* – I use the services you provide. I have views on how you could make them better for me and people in my community. I understand my illness better than you do – I am the one suffering from it. I have views to offer about the way I am treated. Trust me, listen to me, trust my expertise – we can both benefit from this relationship.

2. *Tell me the truth* – I know that the NHS has a strong political influence. I know that there are uncertainties in medical practice. But I have a right to be given the opportunity to understand what these are, to make choices about my care, to be involved in the service I pay for. Share the truth with me.

3. *Nothing about us without us* – You decide on our behalf the services you think we want, and how you think we want them. Ask us; involve us in your decisions. Bring us inside for the benefit of all.

The single most important thing to remember about any enterprise is that there are no results inside its walls. The result of a business is a satisfied customer.

Peter Drucker

CHAPTER SIX

Seeking stability in an unstable world

Seeking stability in an unstable world neatly summarises my view that many managers and staff in organisations want the world to metaphorically "stand still for a day or two" so they can catch up and enjoy some stability and predictability. But:

- **Knowledge, information and speed** force us to carry on at a faster pace – "just to keep up" with the way things are developing and changing. In other words, many want to see a semblance of order, process and structure – but – we live and work in unstructured organisations where those facets simply do not exist any more – a fascinating paradox.

This chapter looks at things from an organisational/management/leadership perspective – but, I suggest, apply in many aspects of our lives in 2003.

My view about coping with the current environment is essentially pragmatic:

- I believe we must **learn to live in the unstable world** of unpredictability – bordering on chaos – then rise above it to a state where we welcome, encourage and celebrate change.

Throughout history, people have risen to challenges. The current Information Technology *"revolution"* presents us another massive challenge. I believe history will record that we are currently living through something as profound as both the agricultural and industrial revolutions.

A few simple anecdotes illustrate the changes.

1. I am old enough to remember the introduction of the **electric** (please note electric not electronic!) typewriter in the early 1970s. At that time I worked as a teenager in a clerical job in my local hospital. The person supervising the typists in our medical records office was an experienced woman approaching retirement. She had been trained and brought up on manual typewriters. She said *"these electric typewriters will never replace the manual"* – **WOW!!** – I wonder how she would feel now – some few years later and a mere "blink of the eye" in historical terms. It seems everyone who has an office desk, has a personal computer as part of their **must have** survival kit. We all do our own word processing – we are all **our own secretary** and we are all producing **self-regulated quality** in the product that comes out of the printer.

2. When I needed a tyre change on the car in the 1980s, the process was:
   - Park the car in the car park of the tyre fitting shop
   - Go into the shop and book in – via a receptionist – the car for a tyre change
   - The receptionist made the appointment and gave me a piece of paper that I took through to the fitter. He fitted the tyre and signed the piece of paper. I took the signed document back to the receptionist who then asked me for payment and she processed the payment.

   The process in 2003 is:
   - I drive my car into the open tyre bay workshop
   - The tyre fitter, fits the tyre, word processes my bill – takes payment and I drive away.

3. **Nowadays, I hardly ever send a letter through the post.** Somehow the process of licking an envelope; folding my letter carefully; placing it in an envelope; licking another piece of paper called a stamp; and then posting that enve-

lope into a box; for someone to – hopefully – deliver, seems an almost antiquated process.

4. **When did I last go to my bank?** I can now manage my finances from the comfort of home via on line banking without reference to another human being. Yet I still remember very well the days when at 3.30 pm on a Friday if you had not got the cash to get you through the weekend then "forget it chum" – the banks were closed till Monday morning. Now if I need cash at 3 am (though god knows why I would need it) I can walk down the road to my nearest cash point and get it.

5. **Could I possibly have even dreamed in my youth that:** "Take away" food would mean anything more than "fish and chips" – or that … not only is there a vast **choice** of take away food – but I can actually sit in my car – order my food, pay for it – then drive round to the other side of the shop to collect it and eat it in the car without even having to exercise my limbs – other than reaching out of the window to pay the assistant. Let me be clear – I am not saying whether this is good or bad – simply that it is reality.

6. As a youngster I saw **patients – complete with their eye patches** – lying in hospital beds for days, as they recovered from their "major surgery" to remove cataracts. Nowadays it is only a slight exaggeration to say patients can "slip away" for an hour at lunchtime, during their busy working day to have cataracts removed through laser surgery.

7. When the **NHS Plan** was launched in the House of Commons in July 2000, I printed a copy from the Web of the Speech of Alan Milburn, Secretary of State for Health, **before he had sat down in the Commons delivering the speech**. My mind drifts to the "old days" of five years previously when – if I was really lucky – I might have seen a hard copy of such a speech – as part of some massive circulation list in the office. In reality I probably would not have seen it

at all. **The difference? – I was in control of accessing the material.**

What does all this mean?

The choices that we face are complex and yet simple.

One choice is to hope that things will one day return to the rational, logical, ordered and well structured days of the past in organisations. Some will remember those days, when, it seemed, the mechanistic approach worked. There were processes based largely on order and logic, and if followed, had a fairly predictable outcome.

A second choice is to **embrace the change**. This will mean shelving our fond memories and affection for the "good old days" (by the way THESE are the good old days) when "we knew what was going on in this place." It means **acknowledging and believing** that the current climate provides us an opportunity and not a threat. It is more than simply a positive mindset, seeing the glass as half full and being an optimist. It is **positively** using the opportunity that speed of access to information presents us with. Nowadays we can access almost anything we want via search engines on the web. This is phenomenal power if used wisely and ethically.

So which option do we choose?

The answer will be an individual decision for all of us. Of course, there will be other options for individuals. I am not wishing to simplify such a complex issue to choosing one of the two options outlined here.

In trying to summarise this paradox, my view is pragmatic. I look around and recognise that **this is not 1969** when I started work in a much more predictable, rational, logical and structured organisation called the National Health Service. Over 30 years later the organisation is still called the National Health Service but it has changed dramatically.

The world outside the NHS is changing; the customer is potentially, and in many cases, literally as knowledgeable as the traditional "expert." In my opinion, it is simply not helpful to debate whether this is a good or bad thing. It is a fact.

I don't think **"burying our head in the sand to this change"** is a helpful position to take. I support the view of embracing the change – turning it into an opportunity and by using the opportunity ethically in all that we do, learn to celebrate the change it brings.

I recognise the need to accept and respect all choices of individuals in this debate. The older I get, the more uncomfortable I become, with words like "right", "wrong", "good" and "bad".

Accepting difference is the expression that nowadays fits more neatly in my study of leadership, change management and generally how things get done – whether talking about organisational or personal life.

Recently I started a new trend without realising it. In the course of my job I attend many meetings – I chair quite a few.

I decided – completely randomly – one day that we would not have an agenda for one meeting and instead I asked people to simply say what they felt we needed to discuss. I went round the room in turn asking people and we wrote their topic up on the flipchart. We had a long list and then we agreed the most important. We discussed them in order of agreed priority. We managed the time available.

This seemed an eminently sensible approach and team members seemed to like it. The cynics of course felt this was not acceptable and that important business would not be covered if we did not think about the agenda in advance. It was not surprising to me that the agenda agreed in "real time" on the day did actually cover all that we would have planned in a traditional agenda and probably more.

This is not rocket science and it is not a universal truth that all meetings should or can be organised in this way. However **meetings are work** and they must be productive with outcomes. This method means that those round the table bring their current energy, enthusiasm and mood to the table.

All I am asking is for you to give it a try – you may be surprised by the outcome. So far the concept has been taken on board by a couple of folks who work with me and they like it. They feel it is more productive than the traditional meeting. I agree.

CHAPTER SEVEN

No boundaries

If you work in an office nowadays I don't think you have to have a degree in sociology to realise something is "going on".

We are going through something that is challenging basic beliefs and values in the office setting. I see it, hear it and experience it everyday. I cannot be alone.

I was discussing with colleagues how we are now in an environment where a quality broadsheet newspaper can be produced in the spare bedroom of anyone skilled enough to use a computer. Yes, of course, the paper then needs printing ... but wait ... Andrew Lavender a young IT Manager going places said "Does it actually need to be printed? Why not have virtual readers only."

AN AHA MOMENT
Old language "read the paper" new language "read the screen".

It made me think about the world of office work twenty years from now. I am not into science fiction but what I am writing "feels" a bit like that.

The youngsters of today ... and by that I mean six and seven year olds ... have keyboards as extensions to their fingers. It is amazing to try and predict the world of office based work for them. When I think back 20 years in my career it is simply unrecognisable from today.

When I was a young in the 1970s everything was paper-based. The computer was something that was being talked of "coming to an office near you". People were moderately interested and were prepared to see it as a marginal piece of office equipment that might possibly help them, but most did not really see it as anything but a futuristic piece of kit being promoted by a few eccentric folks in the office. **What an understatement that turned out to be.**

Then along came the World Wide Web and E-mail. Nowadays if I want anything my first thought is not to ask the boss … it is to log on to Google and do a search. This might range from:

- That particular report I want … to …
- How much cheaper can I find that holiday I want by shopping around? … to …
- What is the most effective current treatment for a complicated medical condition?

The point is not about trying to be clever, or smarter than the next person, simply that there are now **no boundaries**. We can ask **what** we want and we do not have to ask a particular expert. We simply ask the world the question and sure enough there will be someone in the world that can provide the answer. I am not making a judgement about whether the answer is correct but the days are certainly gone when one must see the truth as being the sole province of one "expert in the field".

Why are patients turning up at consultations with challenging questions for the health professionals? The answer is complex but one reason must be access to information that all human beings now have – literally at their fingertips. For those of you around my age (52) reading this book who, like me, have a mother and a daughter just think about the relationship that exists between your mother and her GP and your daughter and her GP. Without generalising I suspect that in most cases there is a different relationship. The younger person will be armed with questions – their expectation will be more challenging to the doctor. I think that is good. There is nothing better to keep us on our toes and "ahead of the game" than to be challenged to justify what we say.

As always … we have choices about all this:

Choice Number One – Accept the new world of IT driven office settings and learn to accept it then learn to love it, then learn to call for more change;

or

Choice Number Two – Refer to Choice Number One.

The days of rationality and having lots of time to debate issues have gone. Of course many people want things to move at the more leisurely pace they have become accustomed to in their career. The snag is the demands are different. We used to work in a situation where the customer did not drive the process. The customer responded to the foibles of the organisation. The customer today is calling the shots and is, in fact, in charge. And, by the way, **the customer wants it NOW**.

Smart organisations are always ahead of the customer – historically the best performing organisations have wonderful relationships with customers. The new world means that organisations need to be very smart to be ahead of the customer.

Imagine this scenario:

I have a budget to buy my new printer – say £100. I go along the high street to Retailer A – the printer I want is available for £100 … I go two doors down the street to Retailer B – the same printer – also available for £100. What is it that will make me part with the £100 – probably the way I feel about the shop and the way I am treated by the sales folks.

As if that is not challenging enough for retailers … now imagine a further complication for both Company A and Company B.

I sit at home in my cupboard now converted to an office … go online to a whole range of sites to seek out the best price for the identical printer … not only is it £20 cheaper … it will be delivered within 48 hours to my home. I complete the sale online.

I have concluded the purchase without leaving the warmth and comfort of my home. I did not have to pay for the privilege of parking my car in the local car park, walk in the cold and rain to two shops. Now tell me the world is not changing.

I am just reading Re-imagine … Tom Peter's latest book. It is full of examples of how the IT revolution is radically changing the world of the "white collar" worker. Peters estimates that 80% of white collar jobs – as we now know them – will either disappear entirely or be reconfigured beyond recognition in the next 15 years!!! … that is staggering … but then Peters quotes the Chief Executive of General Electric who says that "75% of GE administrative and back-office jobs will disappear within **3 years!!**"

I believe the massive cultural challenges that are created by this information technology revolution should be faced head on and celebrated. There is simply no point in denying the existence of the new order of things.

Our children are being brought up surrounded by massive leaps of technological advance that do feel like science fiction … they are going to arrive on the work scene ten years from now with a totally different view of the world to mine;

- They are going to be more inquisitive
- They are going to bring new skills to the workplace
- They are going to challenge the way things have been done in the past
- They are going to develop a new language that some of us "veterans" will find hard to speak, never mind understand.

Yes of course they are also going to make mistakes … but the mistakes they will be making will be "new mistakes" not repeating the old mistakes that I made and my father made.

There are going to be far more "one person businesses" – call it service industry … call it what you like really – I just think that there will be more people being the **Chief Executive of your own career** in the future. **And again for good measure remember what Charles Handy talked about a decade or so ago. Portfolio careers are here to stay … in our working** lives, one may have several career changes … maybe I am an exception to that rule … 35 years on I am now like Mr Spittlehouse.

I wonder how many youngsters (20 and under) of 2004 will retire having been on the payroll of just one organisation. The days have gone too when one's effectiveness is judged by how long you stayed on the payroll. I suspect that the career of the future will be largely determined by the needs and wishes of the individual in the white collar world, rather than the opportunities presented to them by large organisations.

After 35 years in the healthcare world I am no doubt steeped in NHS management practice. Like many of my peers I swim close to the edge of the pool. What I mean is that I like to consider myself a risk taker, challenging the status quo – but in reality the thought of really challenging root and branch some basic institutional practices is a huge step to take.

Most of us stay near the edge of the pool – it is our comfort zone – rather than swimming out to explore the deep end and risk death through drowning. Perhaps we should learn to be braver and take that risk of going into the deep end more often. After all the edge of the pool can still be in sight – and the chances are we won't actually die.

In summary, my feeling is we should *"get on the bus"* (Tom Peters) and be prepared for a bumpy ride for the next few years … but learn to enjoy the bumpy ride – the smooth ride is an option only for those who wish to remain asleep.

To be pleased with one's limits is a wretched state.

Johann Wolfgang von Goethe

CHAPTER EIGHT

You can call me Sir

I was 17 years old in 1970, and a couple of weeks into my first job in the NHS, when my boss took me aside and told me that when he came into the office he liked to be referred to as "Mr" or "Sir". I seem to recall it felt like a non negotiable condition.

This was his normal behaviour. The other staff … who had worked for him for a while … saw it as perfectly normal too. Recently that got me thinking about how things have changed.

Consider these three contrasts:

- In 1970 every letter that left our office, and those received in our office, was addressed "Dear Mr, Mrs or Miss". In 2004 all correspondence I receive begins either "Dear Trevor", "Hello Trevor", "Hi Trevor" or "Hi". In 2004 most conversations start on first name terms, whether talking to my boss, people I work alongside or someone on the phone I have probably never met.

- In the hospital I worked at in the 1970s there was a "Senior Staff Dining Room" … there was a "Consultant Medical Staff Dining Room" and a "Sisters Dining Room" … there was another Dining Room that did not have a name – this was for the "rest of us". In 2004 most hospitals have one dining room that is for all staff, regardless of rank.

- In 1970 I was expected to wear a collar and tie at work. A suit would be the preferred attire but if not able to afford that, then smart trousers, jacket, shirt and tie was acceptable. The 2004 dress code is different. Those areas away from the "public face" of the organisation are much more liberal about dress code. I do not see as many suits as I used to. Having said that … there are still a high proportion of suits among middle and senior managers in the NHS. Some parts of the NHS allow "jeans day" – usually a Friday of course!

I am not suggesting any of the two distinctly different approaches are right or wrong – that would be presumptuous and arrogant. I simply suggest things have changed dramatically and it is now a very different culture. From memory I was probably comfortable with the old style – it was … after all … "just how it is round here". I am definitely comfortable with the new informality. The "old world" was perhaps one of knowing your place in the pecking order and respect being implicit in the position held by those in all parts of the hierarchy. The new world is more about informality. **However …**

- Would I be comfortable receiving financial advice from a Bank Manager dressed in jeans and T-shirt and a gold stud in his … or indeed **her** (!!!) … eyebrow?

- Would my Doctor inspire confidence … if dressed in sandals, shorts and baseball cap for my consultation?

- Would it feel right to have summer Board Meetings in the garden in the summer with everyone dressed in casual summer outfits drinking ice cool soft drinks?

If the answer to these three questions is no then we might ask ourselves why we feel uncomfortable and where does that come from.

I know this is complex. Our expectations and perceptions about what is expected are deeply rooted in psychology, history and custom. The information technology revolution is one thing that is challenging all our beliefs about issues like the three hypothetical examples above.

I remember reading that as a young man, Bill Gates would – without notice – declare "today is going to be mini-golf day in the office" in the early days of Microsoft – or he would bring in a film so that everyone could watch it – sweets and drinks were provided. This was probably because he did not bring to work a set of preconceived ideas about the way organisations should be run. He brought to work that which we consider to be perfectly normal behaviour outside the hours of 9 am to 5 pm Monday to Friday.

I wonder what would actually happen if Board Meetings were held outside on a nice summer day. Maybe Board Members would find it enjoyable – maybe we are more productive when we are doing something enjoyable. When suggesting such ideas, one is often put into one of three camps:

1   Not in touch with the real world
2   A bit eccentric
3   In need of therapy.

Maybe we need to get more in touch with our child like qualities. In 2004, there is no doubt organisations are faced with some really stark decisions about how to survive in the private sector and, in the public sector, ensuring good quality services at an affordable cost. Traditional approaches to solving problems are always our first position. This is fine but old approaches were for an old world where there was more predictability and stability and we all had more time. The information technology revolution has demanded that we all work at a far quicker pace with the customer no longer a passive recipient of services or goods. The customer is now in possession of information about everything and organisations need to be very smart to stay ahead.

I love the following quotes:

Strategies are Okayed in boardrooms that even a child would say are bound to fail. The problem is there is never a child in the Boardroom."

Victor Palmieri, Fortune, February 24 (1992)

> "
> What a distressing contrast there is between the radiant intelligence of the child and the feeble mentality of the average adult. "
>
> Sigmund Freud

I am a "veteran" of 35 years and steeped in institutional organisations – namely the National Health Service in the UK. I know some of these ideas will have detractors. That is fine – life is all about different views and finding common ground. I like to think I am a "realistic idealist" – how's that for a good old compromise statement? It is like swimming close to the side of the pool ... which is I guess ... where many healthcare managers swim. Close enough to the edge of the pool in case we get out of our depth.

> "
> He who rejects change is the architect of decay. The only human institution which rejects progress is the cemetery. "
>
> Harold Wilson

I am not advocating anarchy, I am simply raising the issue of informality versus formality and to pose the following questions:

- Which of the two approaches results in effective outcomes?
- Does it matter anyway?

CHAPTER NINE

Final thoughts

The title of this book is "Simplicity is the key". I hope as you have read it you feel the title has been justified. It is not intended as a book for academia. It does not set out some grand new and ground breaking leadership or management theory.

I would describe it as "a short book for busy people". I hope it is something you can read on a train journey. I hope it made you smile occasionally. I hope that you felt you could put the book down and pick it up again.

I am convinced that many things in life are made complicated that are really simple. I feel that complexity is an overused word. Complexity is merely the sum of simple parts. I think this is particularly true in the world of leadership and management.

One of my passions is to break down myths of complexity and jargon – management speak.

I try to ask myself with everything I write; "Will my Aunt Doris understand that?" Let me be clear. Aunt Doris may be fictional but I imagine her as a person of average intelligence with rich life experience and much to offer. To show her the respect she deserves I need to make my communication – clear, concise and to the point. I want her to understand it. Of course there will be settings where managers and leaders need to talk "their language" in closed shop sessions but most of the time we should strive to make things clearer. I will put it no more strongly than that.

I have enjoyed writing this book and as stated in the introduction it has been in my head for 20 years. The process of putting together my thoughts and reflections into one book has

> 66
> Nothing is more simple than greatness; indeed to be simple is to be great. 99
>
> Ralph Waldo Emerson

inspired me to want to write more. I want to develop my thinking around story telling, leadership and how teams work.

My experience at work has been in healthcare but I believe the messages contained in this book can be applied in many and varied settings. Where I refer to patients and their carers I believe you can substitute the word customers.

I am delighted to enter into discussions about whether my views are generally applicable and look forward to the communications generated through this book. I am fascinated by the way I now communicate with people "virtually" from all corners of the world. In five years time that will be the norm I have no doubt. There is a tide of progress that excites some and dismays others. My view is essentially pragmatic. I have had to work hard to learn about the way we now communicate through this information technology revolution and I find it both challenging and yet exciting. This is a paradox for all of us.

The best way for you to cope may not be to embrace all this as your "best friend." I do feel however that, embrace it we must – even if only as an "occasional acquaintance." Individuals will see this information revolution as an opportunity or a threat – many will not actually care.

I simply see it as an opportunity that we can make work for us. We must always remember the power of the spoken word. The eye contact in conversations will never be replaced by a bland e-mail. Nevertheless if we can see the opportunities presented by "global communication in seconds" then the world become a much more interesting place to be. That is, of course, only my view – you will have your own. The richness and diversity of opinion on this is both its challenge and its charm.

Organisations are undergoing massive change. We face unheralded challenges coming to terms with a totally alien way of working as factors around us change. The nature of work in 1969 is unrecognisable to me today. The culture, the style and the outcomes were all far more predictable, structured and rational.

We are living through something that history will probably record as life changing for people who have lived and worked through the last twenty years.

This book is not a menu for adoption by anyone. It is simply a collection of reflections on where we are now in management and organisations, and, ponders where we might be going. The book is heavily informed by practical management experience.

I suspect the single most important thing I have learned in my working life is that I am still learning.

I have become less and less happy with words like right and wrong and more and more comfortable with words like difference and uncertainty.

I would like to leave you with some important things that have underpinned my work for many years and underpin my reflections in this book. These are things I believe with a passion – not necessarily in priority order:

1. Staff at the front line know all the answers all the time
2. The words "managing people" should be exorcised from the workplace. Nobody manages people anymore – people manage themselves. We manage "things."
3. If a manager has a job at all in 2004 it is to make things easy for staff at the front line
4. I am not convinced leadership can be taught
5. Give all the budget – yes all the budget – to front line staff
6. Forget MBA (Masters in Business Administration) – think MST (Masters in Story Telling)
7. I don't know what a big organisation means in 2004
8. I would take a pay cut for some leaders – I would not work follow some leaders if they doubled my wages
9. Our greatest motivation is always from within.

These nine things and many more in my head are the subject of the next book.

I hope you enjoyed reading *simplicity is the key*.

Bibliography

Bridges W. (2002) *Managing Transitions* (revised edition) Brealey, London
I like this book because William Bridges explains that there are three stages of change. We have to manage "letting go" of the old. We have to manage the "accepting the challenge of the new". In between we have to manage the "transition". If this is not managed people leave and you lose your best people first. There is so much simplicity about this approach. As a non-process person I even liked the process!

Ferguson A. (1999) *Managing My Life.* Hodder & Stoughton
Sir Alex is one of my heroes. He kindly gave me encouraging comments for my book. His autobiography is a book that gave me insight about focus, determination and delivery. It also made me realise that here is a "driven" man with real heart. Small things are important to Sir Alex – it is not just about the big picture. The fact that he took the time to read my book and give me comments about it made him even more of an icon to me. His book is all about action, doing and delivery – not about how things should be.

Hooper A. & Potter, J. (1997) *The Business of Leadership.* Ashgate Publishing Company, Aldershot
This book heavily influenced my thinking about leadership. Alan and John suggest there are seven leadership competencies that can be identified. I just love the way this book was written with examples to illustrate the competencies. It is well worth a read for anyone with an interest in leadership.

Johnson S. (1999) *Who Moved My Cheese.* Vermilion, London
I only recently came across this fabulous little book. It is short simple and straightforward. They are the main reasons I like it. The book also contains a powerful message through a parable about how we can all laugh at ourselves and move on.

Peters T.J. (2003) *Re-Imagine* Dorling Kindersley
This book is wonderful and I hope it will change the whole world of organisations, leadership and management. It will hopefully be seminal in its impact. Peters at his brilliant best ranting about how we must do better. How we must re-imagine everything we do at work – and indeed at home. It is impossible to give it justice in a few

lines but I would say it should be compulsory reading for anyone and everyone who wants to move forward in their career. If you are happy where you are don't bother. But just watch those who do read it move on.

Peters T.J. & Waterman R.H. (1982) *In Search of Excellence*. Harper and Row, New York

This book was an inspiration to me. It made me realise that my views were not out of line. I had felt passionately that everything about management was being made more difficult and complicated than it needed to be. *In Search of Excellence* gave me hope that it really was worth trying to keep things simple.

Roddick A. (1991) *Body and Soul*. Vermilion, London

I just love the way Anita Roddick in this book explained how she had completely dismissed conventional macho male approaches to management to develop the great empire that became The Body Shop. Success was largely down to personal passion and principles of Roddick herself. It is a powerful book about how to get things done and how sometimes the best approach is to go in the opposite direction to everyone else.